Anecdotal Evidence

For Peter Still,
whose scholarship I
have admired for years,
(especially the Berryman
work, + the talk at MLA
about James Wright's poems).
JM Lineberger

Anecdotal Evidence

Jim Linebarger

Drawings by Claude Anderson

Point Riders Press   Norman, Oklahoma

Anecdotal Evidence

© Jim Linebarger, 1991, 1992, 1993.

Acknowledgments:

"After School, Walking Home," "Man with a Gun," "Semi-Formal, 1948," and "The Salesman and the College Boy," *Wormwood Review,* 1991. "Academic Scene," "Doxology," "Essay Question," and "Experienced Teacher Longs for Halcyon Days," *Wormwood Review,* 1992.

"Educational TV, the World of Nature," *Cross Timbers Review,* 1991. "At Last, A True Fable," *The Texas Review.*

"After School, Walking Home," "Man with a Gun," "One Last Drunk," "On Galway Bay," "December, May," "The Jewish Question," "Poetic Justice," "College Lunchroom, the Teachers' Table," "Educational TV, the World of Nature," "Instruction," "Moment of Truth," "Up Front," and "Up Front, First Verse," *The Worcester Poems,* A Trilobite Chapbook, University of North Texas Press, 1991.

Drawings: © Claude Anderson, 1992, 1993.
Cover and Title Page Signet: Xinda Lian
Photo by Emily

ISBN: 0-937280-33-X

Point Riders Press
Cottonwood Arts Foundation
P.O. Box 2731
Norman, OK 73070

Contents

Anecdotal
Evidence

After School, Walking Home

A hot West Texas afternoon, almost summer. Two or three children stand near the porch of a white frame house. Book-satchels hang before them in their hands. There in the open sun a white bulldog lies prone, his stubby legs splayed flat against the ground. A short chain is fastened to his studded collar at one end and at the other to an iron stake. No grass grows in his worn circle of dust and sand. His square jaws grasp the side of the neck of a large, loose-skinned mongrel. This dog has been made to lie with his muzzle pressed against the sand. He whimpers occasionally but no longer tries to struggle. Every minute or so, the bulldog relaxes his jaws but instantly reclenches them, gathering in more of the folded skin. His indifferent eyes are bordered with pink flesh. Blood thickens on the mongrel's coat around the bulldog's mouth. The mongrel cannot move his head. His eyes close and open slowly, looking first at one child, then another. His whimpering is the only sound. No grown-ups are in sight. Not wanting to, the children watch.

Instruction

A father out enjoying a Sunday afternoon drive with his
wife and small son notices the traffic slowing down. He
sees vehicles parked haphazardly along the shoulder of
the heavily-traveled two-lane highway. The father pulls
over and stops. One section of the barbed-wire fence
that parallels the road has been breached. Most of the
women and children stay in their parked cars, but many
of the men get out and hasten to the pasture where a
truck balances oddly on its hood and top. Both its doors
are open wide. The father tells his son to come with him
and takes his hand as they cross the road, step over the
twisted wire and thorny plants, and gather with others
around a man lying on his back alongside the over-
turned truck. This man holds his face in his hands, his
palms cupped over his eyes. He is moaning and rolling
his head from side to side. His face and his hands are
equally bloody. Someone says the ambulance is on its
way. No one seems to know what to do except wait.
The father earnestly explains to the child that a lesson is to
be learned from what they are seeing, something related to
automobiles, speed, drinking, carelessness, death,
responsibility, luck, justice, and fate. The child nods his
head that he understands. The man moans and rolls his
head from side to side. He never takes his hands from
his face.

Moment of Truth

Nighttime. A young husband and wife and their three small children are driving more than a hundred miles to a creek where the husband has only a day and night to fish before he returns to his twelve-hour workday as a meat-cutter in a small grocery store. He will set out trot-lines for catfish. He will not sleep for two days. This is his only recreation, one day off, every few months. The children are snug in the rear seat, and doze to the rumbling sounds of the gently moving car. The husband hums often, but after stopping two or three times to check the trunk, just to be sure all the fishing gear is there, he begins to hum louder, and to sing. The wife says, *You're drinking aren't you? I know you're drinking.* But he swears he isn't. He stops the car again and walks back and opens the trunk. The wife waits, then steps out quickly and sees him raise the flask to his lips. *There,* she says, exasperated, her palms upraised. Like a child, he says, *See, you don't trust me, you never believe me.*

Paperboy

I.   Mornings, the boy sells newspapers at the Army airfield outside town. His regular place is a bench in the messhall. The soldiers let him go through the breakfast line with them, and they kid with him as with a much-younger little brother. If he falls asleep on the bench, they leave the money for the paper on the table beside him, and he always has the right amount when he turns it in. Every morning after breakfast, Tony, one of the cooks, makes a point of bringing him an ice-cream bar, and speaks softly to him. After weeks of summer, the boy gets uncomfortable at being given the ice-cream, so he says he wishes he could do something for Tony. Tony says, Well maybe I could come eat supper at your house sometime. Ask your parents. That night the boy asks his mother and dad, but they are noncommittal until they know more about Tony. The boy doesn't know Tony's last name. The question that seems decisive is about Tony's color, a dark tan. The boy's father says that maybe it isn't a good idea to invite him to the house, but when the boy asks why, the father gently repeats, it just doesn't sound like a good idea.

II.   When the boy tells Tony that he guesses he can't ask him to supper, Tony chuckles oddly and says That's okay. He asks if the boy wants an ice-cream, and says I'm not sure where they stacked them. Why don't you come on back with me and help me find them? The boy gets up from his bench and walks alongside Tony, who has cupped his hand on the back of the boy's neck, his thumb touching the boy's ear. One soldier whistles, shrill, between his teeth, and calls out, Hey, Tony, leave the kid alone, and the others sitting nearby agree. Tony says to the boy, It's okay. Go back to your table and I'll bring it out to you.

At Elmo's Market

The first time was when the produce man handed a
bucket to the butcher-boy and told him to run down to
the drugstore and bring back some cold air. At the
drugstore everyone laughed. The lady there gently
explained to the boy that the produce man was just a
smart-aleck and said to pay no attention to him. The
next time, the produce man cradled in his apron what
looked something like a melting block of ice with heavy
slow-moving white vapor swirling around on its surface.
Here, he said to the butcher-boy, hold this for me. The
boy held the lump only a second before it began to burn
his arms. He dropped it in the sawdust just as Elmo
stepped out of the freezer vault. Elmo's face turned
gray. He shook his head. He said to the produce man, I
told you once to leave this boy alone. Now get your
things and get out.

Semi-Formal, 1948

A junior-high school party and dance at the country
club. Most of the thirteen- and fourteen-year-olds are
inside the mysterious building for the first time. Along
one side of a wide entrance hallway, some bulky objects
have been loosely covered with thick tarpaulins. The
heavy canvas seems out of place amid the expensive
furnishings. The hallway opens into the club-room with
its shiny wooden floor. Near the bandstand is a
Wurlitzer with bubbling lights. The young people are
surprised and pleased that no nickels are needed to play
the records on the machine. The music is Artie Shaw,
Glenn Miller, "Begin the Beguine," "Moonlight
Serenade," and others. The girls wear formal dresses
and corsages bought for them by their mothers. A few
of the boys sport rented tuxedos, but most are in dark
suits with sleeves that reach to their knuckles. The boys
do not know how or when to ask a girl to dance, so a
chaperone crosses the room, takes one of the boys by
the hand, and leads him onto the floor. He doesn't want
to but she insists. After long minutes, other couples join
them, swaying awkwardly and not in time to the music.
Several of the girls must dance with boys who are
embarrassingly short. Two of the boys, fearful of
dancing, and bored, crawl behind the tarpaulins and
discover the slot machines rumored to be there. They
begin to ease nickels into a machine and pull the lever.
After the third coin, a bell clangs and hundreds of
nickels pour out and roll noisily across the dance floor.
Most of the young males cry out in glee, drop to their
knees, and scramble to gather up the coins. The girls
are left standing in mid-dance. They look down at the
boys, then at one another with expressions of chagrin
and resigned hopelessness.

Doxology

The unofficial leader of the youth group at the church is instructing a dozen teen-age boys in their duties at the fund-raising dinner to be held this evening in the Family Life Center. They are to serve the meal and stand around the perimeter of the room throughout dinner and the accompanying prayers and speeches. The leader explains: Just as soon as Brother Jones gives his invitation for free-will offerings, Brother Smith is going to stand up and say he is moved to give a thousand dollars. Then I want all of us, all around the room, to spontaneously break out singing "Praise God from Whom All Blessings Flow." It'll be a great moment for the Lord.

The Jewish Question

A Texan, a freshman at an unnamed Ivy League college on 116th Street in Manhattan where Dwight D. Eisenhower is the figurehead president, is undergoing a probing interview to determine his fitness to belong to a prestigious undergraduate service society. A dozen members interview each candidate, and seek to learn whether he harbors any noticeable deviation from the accepted values of the time. Unknown to the candidate, these include a grave public denunciation of prejudice but in private or among friends telling selected jokes about Negroes, Jews, Southerners, eastern Europeans, Catholics, goyim, women, Puerto Ricans, blue-collar workers, or others not present. One interviewer, hoping to catch him, asks the frosh, "What are your views on the Jewish Question?" His brain scrambles about in near-panic, rushing back to the only two men called Jews he had ever known: one was a stern, efficient doctor, the other a quiet man who always wore black suits and told funny anecdotes. Both spoke with an accent of some kind and sometimes he had difficulty understanding what they said. Beyond that, he can recall nothing, except that a teacher once mentioned that large numbers of Jews had been unjustly killed by Hitler. He figures he has no chance of coming up with an acceptable answer, so he simply admits: "Honestly, I don't understand what you mean. What is the Jewish Question?" Months later, he learns that his un-embarrassed response was considered to be intelligent, forceful, and liberal-minded, and was crucial in his being invited to join the exclusive group.

Up Front

I. At age eighteen, a college freshman with little money, the boy lost his removable-bridge front tooth. At a dime-store, he bought a small triangular file and a dozen or so large buttons of various shades of ivory-white, returned to his dormitory room and, looking in a mirror, matched one of the buttons to the color of his teeth. He filed the button down, with υ cuts along its edges, until he could push it up into the empty slot, to be held there, precariously, by friction. He had to speak gingerly to keep it in place, but at least now he had all his teeth, and they almost matched.

II. The father of a classmate arranged for him to have a date with a pretty Barnard girl. She was eager to please and entertained him with jokes (one about three French cats named Ahn, Duh, and Twah, cats that sank, which baffled him). During the movie, she rested her hand on his knee. Afterwards, he stood with her on the porch of her dormitory, one step down. She put her arms over his shoulders, kissed him, and darted her tongue between his lips, dislodging the button-tooth. "Good-night, lover," she whispered. Trying not to swallow or lose the tooth, the boy curved his closed lips inward, mumbled or moaned something incomprehensible, turned and hurried away.

Poetic Justice

A college junior was taking his first serious literature course and was trying to learn how to read and understand poetry. His professor had suffered some childhood disease which left him unable to walk without crutches. The student often misunderstood phrases in the poems studied, but he did not hesitate to offer any interpretation, however unlikely, that had occurred to him. During the discussion of one involuted stanza, the student pressed too hard and the professor interjected: Young man, please spare us your interpretation. If you will study this passage for twenty years, you will come to the unremarkable conclusion that I am right. Now, can we move on? The student lowered his eyes and stayed quiet. But he continued to consider the poem for several years and became convinced that his reading was one of two or three possibilities. He telephoned the professor, from two thousand miles away, to resume the discussion. But the man had died the preceding year, an apparent suicide.

The Salesman and the College Boy

Easter holiday week, 1955. A college student wearing a sharkskin wool suit, his only suit, has been hitchhiking for two days. He has been rained on and the wool is steamy. A car pulls up beside him and the driver offers him a ride into Memphis. The man is cheerful and talkative. He travels for a plywood company and his business card is made of paper-thin laminated wood. His name is Shelley, spelled the same as the poet. He has just had an unbelievable week of sales and he can't wait to get back home to his wife and family. And to his collie, who also smells pretty gamy when he's wet. He asks the student if he could stand some food. The student says he isn't really hungry, but something is askew in the tone of his voice. The salesman pulls in at a truck stop. At the counter, he orders three hamburgers and two chocolate milkshakes. When the waitress brings them, the salesman sets the double platter in front of the student. The student, both apologetic and proud, says, Thanks, but I can't accept this, I can't pay. The salesman smiles broadly and says, This is America, so I guess even a college boy has a right to be rock-bottom stupid if he wants to. But if you pass out or outright die on me, I'll be late getting home. So if you want to ride with me, eat those hamburgers. The shake is optional. I'll drink it, if you decide you don't want it. The boy eats and drinks, and is pensive.

The New Yorker

At a time when the Pennsylvania Turnpike was the only expressway in the United States: A young male hitchhiker travelling westward is dropped off near the end of the Turnpike, at a poorly-marked place where three roads meet. He holds his thumb out for any vehicle that passes. Finally, one car, with a New York license plate, stops. The driver is confused, lost, and rolls the passenger-side window down slightly to ask the hitchhiker the way to Ohio. The hitchhiker points out the highway and says that's his direction, too, and can he hitch a ride? The driver looks irritated and doubtful, but grudgingly agrees. The driver is a small man and a New Yorker. That is, he is defensive, abrupt, argumentative, a master of the insulting and denying statement, the reddleman of ignorance, the arbiter of social, intellectual, and fashionable superiority, a man certain that out there beyond Jersey is a no-man's land of incestuous retardates, hicks, mutants, and fundamentalists, all craning their necks eastward and longing to move into Gotham where they will destroy civilization as he knows it. Something in his voice sounds as if he may be talking to someone not entirely human, perhaps from a nearby planet or, say, Utah. That may be why the hitchhiker brings the conversation around to the reported dangers to hitchhikers and to drivers picking them up. The driver says, What a load of crap that is. I don't have to be afraid of nuttin', not no fuckin' hitchhikers, and ya wanna know why? I'll tell ya why. I got a fuckin' gun mounted there under that fuckin' floorboard in fronta ya (he points toward the hitchhiker's feet) and a secret trigger that I can pull any fuckin' time I wanna. Any fuckin' hitchhikers fuck with me, I'll blow their fuckin' head off in a fuckin' minute and dump their fuckin' body on the fuckin' road. Not entirely hidden beneath his assertiveness is a pungent residue of fear, like a landfill on Staten Island. The hitchhiker realizes that now there is no way he can put things right. Long miles of silence pass before they get to Cincinnati, where the hitchhiker says, I need to get out here. Thanks for the ride. The New Yorker says Yeah yeah in an indeterminate tone, and drives off before the hitchhiker can close the door. The hitchhiker feels as he always does after an encounter with a New Yorker: somehow, again, he has lost the round, on points.

Man with a Gun

Alone, a young man eats his evening meal, a chili-dog
and milkshake, at one of the stand-up tables in an
uncrowded hamburger joint across from Georgia Tech.
He wears a jacket and tie. In a few mintues he will try
to explain subjects and verbs to hapless adults, most of
them older than he is. He watches as four men wearing
striped prison clothes file in through the front door,
a uniformed guard behind them. Close to his chest the
guard holds a shotgun, his bend sinister. The prisoners'
ankles are lightly shackled, so the men can walk,
clumsily, perhaps even work at mowing grass or picking
up litter, but could never run. The guard pays for chili-
dogs and drinks for himself and the others, and carries
his food to the table where the young man stands. The
guard's unwavering look causes the young man to avert
his eyes. One of the prisoners also brings his food to
the table, but the guard says, *You don't belong up here
with decent people. You go sit down over there.* With
the shotgun, he motions toward a stack of four or five
cases of empty soft-drink bottles. The prisoner says
nothing, shuffles over, and eases himself down on top
of the empty bottles. The guard half-smiles at the young
man as if they share a world of values.

The Question

No one seems to know what happened. In the 1950s, in a town in Georgia big enough to have a country club with a nine-hole golf course and a pool, a local teenager was adjudged to be a source of trouble. Nothing specific, just a certain glance here, a tone of voice there. One morning, his bruised, naked body was found in the pool at the club. The accepted view was that he had sneaked in to go swimming and accidentally drowned. His welts were ignored. The question is, Did that child kick in fear, or did he curse? Or pray? Or beg? The question is, Where are the men with nicknames or initials for names who were present that night? Do they consider how their lives were spent? Do they ever wake up with their own teeth loose and sore from grinding and think of his swollen, lopsided face? The question is, Where were the stars, the moon, that night? The question is.

Gone to Texas

By way of explaining why he chose to move from
Georgia back to Texas, a young man has described to
his uncle some of the incidents he witnessed there, the
gross inequities that blacks suffered, the grinding
injustice, the humiliation. The uncle is an old West
Texan, a man of good will who has worked hard and
steady all his life. He listens politely, nods agreement,
and responds: I know it. And a good nigger'll work as
hard as a good white man. Why I'd rather work with a
nigger any day than with one of them lazy spics from
over there in Meskin-town.

Academic Scene

An avuncular full professor is in charge of this first (and what becomes the last) of a projected series of orientation sessions for the new instructors, all males. He makes a point of calling them gentlemen while he favorably compares the paucity of their educational background to the dearth of their experience in the real world. He explains that they simply do not know how to handle difficult situations and presents them with a hypothetical one: A disgruntled coed comes to your private office (although, of course, none of you are assigned to private offices at this time) and closes the door. She demands a higher grade, which you of course refuse. Then she rips her blouse and begins to shout *Rape!* No one would ever believe your version of what happened. You would lose your position and leave under a cloud. Your career would be ruined. Now just what would you do in a situation like that? A triumphant, intimidating silence. From the back row, a voice like Will Rogers', but younger: Sir, if everything is just like you say, I believe what I'd do is reach over, lock the door, and rape her.

College Lunchroom,
The Teachers' Table

Her thick glasses so enlarge her eyes that she resembles
an owl, blinking slowly and turning only her head from
side to side. Her left hand never leaves her lap except
when it is absolutely necessary. She sponsors one of the
several sororities for Christian girls. She sees absolutely
no reason for all these attacks on custom and traditions.
Negro girls have sororities of their own, and prefer it
that way. And no Jewish girl who is sincere in her faith
could possibly want to join a sorority for Christian
girls. And the sorority is absolutely not interested in
considering anyone who is not sincere in their religion,
irregardless of whom they are.

Lunchroom Revisited

She is middle-aged and imposing: tall and slender,
broad-shouldered, with neatly-coifed hair the white color
and fine texture of a Persian cat's, perhaps dyed but so
expensively done that no one can tell. Her shoes are
from Neiman's. (Everyone knows this because she
generously gives them, barely worn, to young faculty
wives.) She has never spoken an obscenity or vulgarity
in class, and sees no reason for anyone ever to do so.
The discussion shifts to the seven deadly sins. After
some Sisyphean efforts, they are agreed upon. She
states catetgorically that she has never committed any
of them and in fact has never been tempted to do so.
The quiet is broken only by the unintentional sounds of
utensils against plates, ice in tea glasses, a throat not
quite cleared, overhead fans whirring unevenly.

Revenge

I. Early in a West Texas high-school football game,
a defensive back is running alongside a receiver from the
opposing team. The pass is overthrown and falls
incomplete. After the whistle, the defender slows, stops,
and turns around to trot toward the line of scrimmage.
Suddenly his legs are hit from behind and buckle under
him. After some time, he is helped to hobble off the field
and does not return to the game. The game-film shows
that the receiver continued downfield, turned around
and, checking to see if any officials were nearby, built up
speed and drove his shoulder into the knees of the
defensive back.

II. Twenty years later, the former back has become a teacher at a university that has a mediocre football team. He slightly favors one leg as he walks. The college is looking for a new head coach and the former receiver, now coaching at a small college in the Rockies, applies for the position. When the teacher reads the man's name in the school paper, he writes a letter to the athletic committee describing the incident and requesting that they inquire carefully into the coach's background. It is discovered that, as an assistant in earlier years, the coach had slapped a player during practice and was instantly fired. He doesn't get the job. Over the years, the teacher had fantasized elaborate forms of retaliation. But now he learns that one of the committee members remarked that twenty years is a long time to hold a grudge, and finds himself left not simply with feelings of pleasure and self-justification. He is also baffled by a new sense of his own pettiness, and embarrassed that others are aware of it.

Experienced Teacher
Longs for Halcyon Days

One of his bouffant sophomores, a blond and blank P.E. major from his old West Texas high school, interrupted the teacher's peripatetic remarks with *"Please* don't tell us about those six million Jews or about the forty thousand men, women and children who starved to death in the world today or how many jillions or trillions it cost us to fight in some silly war." Her voice was not really aggressive. Long suffering. Resigned. Slightly disgusted. Weeks later, when the teacher asks for an example of religious intolerance, she voluteers: she and her high-school friends were forced to eat cafeteria fish on Fridays, and all because of the Catholics. The teacher sighs. He longs for one of his old, easy jobs, as the hot-tar man on a roofing crew, or digging caliche with a shot-shovel. Maybe he could have been a straw-boss by now.

Supermarket

Rummaging through the pears, all of them as hard as
the stones in the Frost poem, I glance up and see a
familiar face, one from the university, a graduate student
perhaps, though not one I've ever taught or met. He
nods and says hello. I ask him how things are going.
He's teaching at a junior college somewhere up near the
Oklahoma border. Five classes, all freshman composition.
He completed his Ph.D. here at the university two years
ago. His job is temporary, no chance for tenure. He
must be in his mid-thirties. Next semester, he plans to
enter a school of chiropractic medicine. It will take him
four more years. But then he will be able to make a
living for himself and his wife, and they want to have
children. They will be able to move anywhere in the
country. I tot up my thirty-five years of teaching, of
thinking I was doing honest and useful work. He is
friendly and resigned. He faces his future with a shrug
and a shy grin.

A True One, for Friends

Not even the names have been changed. Jim was the kind of guy who insisted on doing favors for others and volunteered his help even when it wasn't needed. He was always punctual and responsible. So when the battery on his perfectly-maintained car went dead, unexpectedly, inexplicably, in downtown Denton, and he was scheduled to teach a class in twenty-two minutes, he panicked, until he remembered his friend Don, who owned the antique shop on the square. He could get a jump-start from him. At the shop, Warde, a mutual friend of the two, a casual, relaxed man with wide interests and a love of blarney, was chatting with Don, sparring about the prices of rugs. When Jim explained his problem to the two of them, Don at first said he would close the store and bring his truck over immediately. But then he suggested that maybe Warde could help and he wouldn't have to close the shop. Warde looked vaguely away, then at his watch, and said something about needing to drop by the bank and run some other errands. Livid, Jim coldly said, Bill you low-down son-of-a-bitch. I've helped you a dozen times, anytime you asked me and sometimes when you didn't, and now, when I need you, you say you're just too damn busy to help me out. Don looked uneasy, Warde became immediately apologetic, and said *Sure, sure I'll help,* without any edge to his voice. The jump-start worked, and Jim made it to his class barely in time. Next morning, Jim was munching cereal, and brooding. The phone rang. It was Warde: *Hi Jim. I'm just calling to say that I've got a few minutes before I need to be at work, and I, uh, was just wondering if maybe you had anything you wanted me to do.* His tone was normal, with no hint of irony. Taken aback, Jim was finally able to say, Warde, you chicken-shit son-of-a-bitch. I ain't letting you off the hook that easy. I ain't *ever* gonna forget this, you sorry bastard. He tried not to but couldn't keep from laughing. Warde stayed quiet until the laughter subsided. *Well if you need me today, I'll be at my office all morning. But if you think of anything, just leave a message with my wife.* His voice was not laughing, only smiling. Jim said, Warde, you can't get away with this. I'll kill you for this, I swear—but Warde had already said *Bye* and clicked off.

Educational TV,
The World of Nature

A relaxed, resonant voice smoothes over the casual death of one animal, and then another. At last a feckless fawn escapes, only by chance. All this is said to be necessary in a world governed by fixed laws if balance, order, and harmony are to be maintained in nature. For example: an expressionless snake glides rhythmically toward a frog twice his diameter. The frog does not blink. The snake strikes, and grasps the frog's elliptical snout. The frog seems as preoccupied and uninvolved as the snake. The snake's unique ability to dislocate his lower jaw is noted, as a curiosity. In leisurely gulps, the snake begins to swallow the frog, still alive, who kicks feebly. Slowly the frog becomes only a rounded lump just behind the snake's head. A string of sticky eggs hangs from the snake's mouth. He flicks his tongue, and is still. After a pause, the audience is sincerely invited to observe in future weeks a continuing series of such exemplary natural events. These programs are recommended by impeccable organizations, are made possible by grants from discriminating blue-chip corporations, and are approved for viewers of all ages.

Essay Question: Art or Reality?

In England, during the first half of the nineteenth century, one particular male child was trained in the art of sketching and ultimately achieved a proficiency approximately equal to that of the young ladies of the time who were instructed in music or needlepoint as part of their preparation for marriage. He was educated privately, and both pampered and ruled by a protective mother. He traveled extensively throughout Europe and later proclaimed that, for pure natural beauty, Friar's Crag in the Lake District was unsurpassed. After a proper engagement with a suitable partner, he married. But on his wedding night he discovered to his horror that his bride had hair in places his aesthetic sensitivity could never have imagined and his sensible vision could not bear to gaze upon. The marriage was annulled, and he seems to have concluded that his near-wife's peculiar secondary characteristics were probably endemic among females. Through the rest of his long life, the man continued to read widely, to publish extensively, to lecture to breathless audiences. He became the pre-eminent aesthetician and art critic of his age. He also became obsessed with female children as objects of beauty. No one seemed to notice any irony in this situation. Even after the details of his wedding night became known, he continued to be touted as one whose visual sensibilities and overall aesthetic judgment were superior. Explain why, or at least point out how this man's story is similar to a drama by Samuel Beckett or to any wildly absurd and sadly hilarious sketch by Lenny Bruce.

Rate of Exchange *

Ha. In London, in the spring of 1944, a tactician in the
OSS hit upon a plan to mislead the Nazis about where
the cross-channel invasion would occur. So, secretly, a
member of the Dutch underground was brought to
England, where he was fed misinformation and then sent
back to Holland. Someone made sure the Gestapo
knew where to find him. After torture, no one can guess
at his pain, he told them what he knew. To be doubly
sure, the OSS provided the same information to another
unsuspecting Dutchman. He too was betrayed to the
Nazis, who took him to a concentration camp where he
died. (The details are sketchy.) The men were named
Henk Janssen and Jan Bakker; let's try to forget the
name of the OSS man in charge. After the war, the
families of the two men were paid cash money by the
U.S. government. And my only question is, ha, just how
was that cash figure arrived at? And what was the exact
amount? Ha. And offhand, how much would you
estimate that to come to, in today's dollars?

* See Arthur Widder's *Adventures in Black* (New York:
Scholastic Book Services, 1962), pp. 85-90.

Sheepish

Early in June. Exhilarated in the cool, sunlit air, an
American tourist energetically pedals his bicycle out of
Dublin, headed west. The narrow tires hum smoothly
on the damp pavement, and he considers trying to make
it to Galway in two days. But by late morning, his
sinuses begin to bother him, so he settles into a more
leisurely pace. Soon, off in the distance, he hears shouts
and laughter. He rides past a meadow cordoned off with
green and white streamers. There, red-faced children
are enjoying a field day of races and games. Men in
woolen jackets and ties and caps supervise the activities,
and often cheer-on one child or the other. The tourist
rides on into the village and stops at the first B&B
sign. He showers, changes to his slacks and loafers, and
walks back to the meadow. He spends the afternoon
there, sauntering from event to event, nodding to the
adults and chatting with the children. The men are
friendly, and greet him with "Fine day" or "Lovely
day." The children are delighted with the stranger as he
tries to pronounce their names and the name of the
village, Monasterevan. On the way back, he notices
"I.R.A." and "BRITS OUT" painted crudely on the
balustrade of a bridge. In the village, he tries the door of
the pub, and it's open. He steps over a raised threshold
and into the dim light. His eyes make out a woman
staring at him, bristling in outrage or disgust. She snorts,
says good-bye to the three young men sitting at the bar,
and flounces past him out the door. He supposes that
she has mistaken him for a Britisher. He stands next to
the three men, slightly apart. They glance at him
noncommittally, until he orders a pint of Guinness;

then they seem friendlier. He looks at them and says "Lovely day" in his slowest Texas accent. The young man nearest him says *So you're from America.* Yes, from Texas. *Oh. Hmmm. I suppose there are lots of cows in Texas?* Yes, everywhere. Cows and ranches and cowboys. *Hmmm. But not many sheep, eh?* No, not too many sheep. By now the other two are casting sly looks at each other, trying to suppress chuckles, one clutching his forearms to his stomach as the other wipes tears from his eyes and lightly bangs his fist against the lip of the bar. One tries to repeat "Not many sheep," but he can't complete the phrase between gasps of stifled laughter. The visitor is at first baffled and uncomfortable, then irritated, and asks the nearest young man if he has said something wrong. Immediately the Irishman is apologetic, and elbows his companion and shushes him, but the man can't stop. Abruptly, the American says *Well I hope you boys have a nice day,* and leaves. Only later, back in his room, does he notice the generous slab of moist dung and straw wedged against the heel of his shoe. He goes outside and scrapes it off. That evening, brazen in his embarrassment, he returns to the pub. Now, it is crowded, and some of the men recognize him from the afternoon and chat with him. The talkative young Irishman is there and greets him with measured, careful politeness. The other two, anxious and unsmiling, studiously avoid him, edging away whenever he seems to be drifting in their direction.

On Galway Bay

I. Despite having a reserved ticket, an American tourist
and his bicycle have just been kept from boarding one
of the tug-like ferries that shuttle between Galway and
the Aran Islands. No other departures are scheduled
for twenty-four hours. The deckhand in charge of
loading the vessel informs the tourist that neither he
nor his bicycle will be welcome aboard, ticket or no,
until the unlikely occurrence of a specified event in an
unimaginably cold hell of a remote place and time. The
American pedals off furiously, headed for Dublin.
Fifteen miles later, winded and calmer, he decides to
lodge a complaint against the deckhand, and so he
rides back to Galway, to the Tourist office. There, all
are dismayed that an American visitor in Ireland has
been treated so unpleasantly; they insist that he journey
to the Islands as their guest.

II. The next morning, on the bridge of another ferry. The Captain has invited the American, his guest, to chat with him as they ride the choppy sea. Captain Paddy is jovial, solicitous, and does not mention the incident. The passenger comments on the polite, friendly nature of the Irish, especially when they are compared to, say, Americans. He remarks that the deckhand is the only Irishman who had ever been rude to him. Captain Paddy, relieved that the subject has been broached, says, "It was shameful, what that man did, terrible. But the poor man himself, mind you, he's not an Irishman, not truly Irish." He pauses, "You see, the man himself, he's from Boston."

Ladies' Night at the Broken Spoke

I've seen her here before. Usually she's with an older
man whose belt-buckle holds up his stomach and whose
trousers drape over his shrunken haunches. Tonight
she's alone. She asks me to dance, a slow one by Garth
Brooks. She is nearly six feet tall. She lost nearly thirty
pounds over the past two years. She has two kids,
nearly grown. The man she used to date, he lost his wife
nearly five years ago and she felt sorry for him. He can't
dance good at all. They've been seeing each other for
nearly three years but it's over. Her eyes keep looking
back at the front door. She is clumsy and her hair smells
of ammonia. She has a massive jaw, like Primo Carnera's.
Next night, the man comes in alone and sits beside me.
Tears in his eyes, he says he's decided to live, after
all. She's told him she wants to move to El Paso with
some guy who has kids of his own and listen to this she
says his mother says she's going to buy them a house so
they can be a real family. Can you believe that? This
guy can't hold a job and he's already been married three
times. *Aw they're all just bitches anyway,* he says.
Except for my wife, rest her soul.

Two-Timin', Honky Tonk Woman

From the syncopating jukebox, Waylon and Willie are
extolling the virtues of a good-hearted woman. Sitting
alone, a middle-aged man is waiting for the band to start
before he asks anyone to dance. But a petite woman
with jet-black hair does a little two-step as she walks by
his table, so he asks her. Up close, she looks more
nearly his age. She pushes her small breasts against him
and she stumbles as she dances. Her mouth has
difficulty forming words, even in slow-motion: She isn't
out on a date with that guy she's sitting with, and she's
paying for her own drinks, so she can dance with
anybody she wants to and even if he *is* her boss he can
just go to hell if he don't like it. But she's broke right
now and needs to borrow twenty dollars to party
tonight, and this ring is worth a thousand dollars and he
can keep it until she makes it good. And she can really
be nice to him too, if he knows what she means. She
says, Okay, Tall-Drink-o-Water, just *ten* dollars, that's all
I need. Does a big-spending blue-eyed stud-hoss like you
have ten dollars? She bets he don't but wishes he
did. He is confused by her mixture of insults and
flattery, coquetry and disdain. He waves the ring aside
and takes ten dollars from his pocket (She says, Don't
let nobody *see* it). He says, This is a gift, not a loan, and
he wonders why he did it. A week later she comes in
again with her boss. She walks past his table and
says, "Hello, Sugar-daddy." She smiles out of one corner
of her mouth. She glances up at her boss and winks.

Common Story

When they married, she was just out of high school. He was ten years older, a respectable man with a good job. Within three years, they had two daughters. The wife was a virgin at marriage and assumed that her husband's preference for masturbation was just the way men were. But over the next ten years, he spent more and more of his free time locked in the garage restoring his '39 Ford coupe. Feeling guilty, she searched the car, not knowing what she was looking for, and discovered a cache of magazines and photographs of nude adult males with female children, some near-babies. Heartsick and confused, she soon took a one-day-a-week lover. The marriage continued for years, almost as before, except that she was careful never to leave her daughters alone with their father.

December, May

The woman is fifty-seven and still pretty. The man is
bearded and about to be thirty-four. He has two young
sons from his second wife. (He says he's really scared of
AIDS, and that woman was running around on him.) He
tells this woman how easy-going and comfortable she is,
not like the others. He says he loves her. She loves him
and his boys. He works two jobs, odd hours. On his
birthday, happy, she decides to fix his favorite cake and
surprise him with it at work. She tells the boys to come
along with her to wish their daddy a happy birthday. But
he isn't at that job. He isn't at the other job, either. She
drives by his second wife's place. His pickup is parked
alongside her trailer, pulled in close.

Up Front, First Verse

The man was nearly middle-aged before he realized that, throughout his childhood, he had an unconscious but persistent need for self-injury as a means of securing his mother's affection. Before he was three, at a monument works, he pulled a small tombstone over onto his feet. At five, he began regularly jumping from housetops, pretending to fly. When he was six, he ran to straddle a tire, one of his toys, and could not help rolling over onto his face, knocking a front tooth out against the sidewalk. During a game of childhood tackle-football, a thumbnail was raked off as it caught on a chain-link fence (he couldn't decide whether to take the thumbnail along to show to his mother). At ten, he jumped from a tool shed and yanked out another front tooth, a permanent one. (The tooth projected slightly, and was snagged on a wire clothesline he had forgotten was there.) At twelve, walking on a horizontal water pipe suspended four feet or so off the ground, he slipped and fell, straddling the pipe. In later years he would recall no pain during these mishaps, but only the pleasure of being comforted.

Land of Dreams

The steps of the stairway are more than eight feet tall,
and so the young man can barely jump high enough to
get a finger-hold on the next tread and pull himself
up. He is exhausted and has lost track of how many
steps he has climbed. He looks upward and sees the
stairway curving out of sight, as in two facing
mirrors. Out of habit, he checks his watch, which he
always wears on the inside of his wrist. It is not
there. He can't tell whether he has forgotten it,
misplaced it, or the sneak-thief has taken it, the one who
has so often stolen from him in the past. Where the
watch should be, a bloodless slit in the skin is forced
apart from inside and a pair of inch-long, dark-brown
cockroaches crawl out and scurry off, skittering as if
they have been sprayed with insecticide. He looks back
down the stairs. At the bottom, far off, a mature woman
looks up coldly. She points to the serrated carving knife
which the man, no longer young, holds in his right hand.
He looks at it, down at his flaccid penis, and again at
her. She smiles, nods, and stretches out her hand to
him, palm up. She has an imploring, demanding look on
her face, but he pretends to be confused about what she
wants him to do.

One Last Drunk

Near dawn, a man has been awake all night drinking uncounted beers but also taking vitamin pills so that he can stay healthy. He reaches for his wallet and keys and tries to leave his room to buy more beer. But squatting just inside the door is a green, mechanical frog as large as a hand with fingers extended. Unblinking, the frog stares at the man, not directly, slightly askance. As the man moves to sidle around him, the frog hops sideways just enough to block the way, and waves open his mouth to reveal an upper and lower row of metal teeth, triangular and bright as chrome. The man knows that the frog is not there, and tells him so. The frog has a blank look. Keeping his distance, the man tosses a bandanna over the creature, covering it entirely. Under the bandanna, nothing moves. Just to be sure, the man waits a full minute, then jerks the bandanna aside. The frog is gone. Relieved, the man looks again toward the doorway. Standing there is a sickly-thin, snaggle-toothed neighbor with a strange cast in one eye. He is smiling as if he has a sinister secret.

June 7, 1990

Even my father, no great man, had a last fine day
as himself. That afternoon he looked tired, but he
said he was just lazy. An evening of laughter and
friends, a heavy dinner thick with beef and gravy
and bread, the kind of meal he always liked, and
the chatter of women, giggling beyond their years,
the men like brothers, all lying to one another
about miles per gallon and how hard they used to
work. When it was time to go home, he said
*Something's wrong. I guess I need to sit down
a minute.* Two women cradled his head as it
leaned to one side. *Call Jim,* he said.

At Last, A True Fable

Only now, after long grief, are six middle-aged
daughters finally able to talk with one another
about their father, a kind and good man, as men
go in a world that leans and wobbles. They have
gathered around a solid-oak table in a sunlit dining
room. After a silence, one tries to apologize to the
others: You know, he was always partial to me,
and that must have hurt all of you, deeply. I'm so
sorry for that, but I did love him so very much,
as much as he loved me. Another silence, then
outbursts of confused questions and asseverations.
Almost at once, the six begin to realize that each
of them believed, always, that she was her father's
particular pet and that the others must have been
heartbroken not to be his favorite. At their
moment of awareness, if a white dove had flown
across the sky as sign or symbol, who could mind?

Jim Linebarger grew up in West Texas, went to Columbia on a football scholarship, took courses there from Trilling, Bentley, Dupee, Tindall, and others. He teaches at the University of North Texas in Denton. He wrote the first book-length study of John Berryman (Twayne, 1974). His poetry books include *Five Faces* (Trilobite, 1976) and *Texas Blues* (Point Riders Press, 1989).